Teaching the Parrot

other books by Richard Edwards

THE WORD PARTY
(Lutterworth/Puffin, 1986/87)
WHISPERS FROM A WARDROBE
(Lutterworth/Puffin, 1987/89)
A MOUSE IN MY ROOF
(Orchard/Puffin, 1988/90)
THE HOUSE THAT CAUGHT A COLD
(Viking/Puffin, 1990/91)
LEOPARDS ON MARS
(Viking, 1993)

Teaching the Parrot

RICHARD EDWARDS

illustrated by John Lawrence

faber and faber
LONDON · BOSTON

First published in 1996
by Faber and Faber Limited
3 Queen Square London WC1N 3AU

Photoset by Wilmaset Ltd, Wirral
Printed and bound in Great Britain by
Mackays of Chatham PLC, Chatham, Kent

A CIP record for this book
is available from the British Library

ISBN 0-571-17941-X

10 9 8 7 6 5 4 3 2 1

Contents

Teaching the Parrot, 3
John Spoon, 4
After Dark, 5
The Vision of the Minister of Transport, 6
Copped, 7
Match of the Night, 8
Nathaniel, 11
Mr Williams, 12
The Lugworm and the Haddock, 14
Don't Blame Me, 16
One Dark Night, 17
The Comet and the Moon, 20
Eileen Idle, 22
Ambition, 23
In a Narrow Place, 26
Clearing Out, 29
The Witches Are All on Strike, 30
The Cow in the Storm, 32
Awake, Asleep, 34
A Visit to Harley Street, 37
The Magic Drum, 39
Over to Our Reporter on the Front Line . . ., 40
Professor Mysterious, 42

Finding Out about the Family, 46
Andy Handy, 48
There Were These Woodworm, 49
Moira Murray, 50
Whose Job It Is, 51
The Wildfowler's Nightmare, 53
Shaggy Dogs, 54
Benny Penny, 56
Sow What, 58
Witch of the Waterland, 59
Miss Antrobus, 62
Mammoths, 64
A Bargain, 65
My Pet Mouth, 66
Magroodle Said, 68
Windfalls, 70
Blankets, 72
Little Cissie Wilson, 73
The Anaconda, 74
Breakfast for One, 75
Old Alf, 76
Just for Fun, 77
Joe Bright, 80

TEACHING THE PARROT

Teaching the Parrot

'Say Polly,' whispered Laurie,
But her parrot wouldn't speak.

'Say Polly,' urged Laurie,
And she stroked her parrot's beak,
'Say Polly,'
But her parrot wouldn't speak.

'Say Polly,' begged Laurie,
'Say Polly, will you, please?
Say Polly,' ordered Laurie,
And she got down on her knees.
'Say Polly,' hissed Laurie,
'Come on, just a little squeak,
Say Polly!'
But her parrot wouldn't speak.

'Say Polly,' growled Laurie,
'Just the once and just for me.
Say Polly!' shouted Laurie,
'You're a stupid parrot, see!
Say Polly!' bellowed Laurie,
'Or I'll pluck you for my tea.
Say Polly!!' wailed Laurie,
As the tears rolled down her cheek,
'SAY POLLY!!!' . . .

But her parrot wouldn't speak.

John Spoon

John Spoon dressed up in camouflage,
In brown and blotchy green,
And lay down in a grassy field
To keep from being seen.

But camouflage is dangerous,
And camouflage is how
Poor Johnny Spoon one afternoon
Got eaten by a cow.

After Dark

Mog is dreaming of being a real cat
With a deadly slink
And a mouthful of feathers.

Mrs Hippo is dreaming of a warm lagoon in
   Africa
And floating weightlessly
Under an orange moon.

Peter is dreaming of letting the fox get close
And then outwitting him
With a perfect somersault.

Blackeyes is dreaming of being holed up
In a bamboo forest
And eating his slow way out.

Barney is dreaming of swiping salmon
From ice white streams in the Rockies
And never missing one.

Brock is dreaming of a wet night in the bluebells,
Endless earthworms,
And the crunch crunch crunch of snails.

The Vision of the Minister of Transport

Roads, build me roads, build me roads!
Roads are the love of my life!
Build them all over
From Dingwall to Dover
Roads cutting straight as a knife.

Roads, build me roads, build me roads!
Cover the whole earth in grey!
No ragged edges,
No fields, no hedges,
Shove those woods out of the way!

Roads, build me roads, build me roads!
Nothing but roads and the sky!
Concrete, not trees,
Who needs birdsong or bees?
Badgers and byways?
No! Bridges and highways.
Foxes and grasses?
No! Flyovers, bypasses.
Won't life be sweet
When the world's one big street
Where we live and we drive till we die?
Roads, build me roads, build me roads!
It's roads they'll remember me by.

Copped

The policeman was all bleary-eyed
From getting out of bed,
He fumbled with his razor,
The shaving foam turned red –
He winced into the mirror,
'You're nicked,' the policeman said.

Match of the Night

Good evening. Here in Wembley Wood
A full moon gleams
As fans for the Cup Final
Prepare to greet their teams.
There's chanting from some field mice
A stoat's beating a drum,
The rabbit referee runs out
And here the teams come!

All set. The rabbit whistles
And the game gets under way,
The badger to the hedgehog
To the hare, oh, he can play!
He dribbles round two weasels,
He cuts into the box,
Sidesteps, sells a dummy,
But gets flattened by the fox!

It's got to be a penalty,
Yes, the ref points to the spot,
The badger runs up, takes it,
And scores with a swerving shot.
The game restarts, tight marking,
Now the rat goes on a run,
He floats a good cross over,
Squirrel nods it in. 1 – 1!

Half time. They take a breather.
A substitution's made –
The rat spiked by the hedgehog
Limps off to get first aid.
This second half's a thriller,
Now what's happening? It's a card,
A red one – for the fox for tackling
Late and much too hard.

The rabbit checks his watch:
There's just a minute left to go,
The hare picks up the ball now
From the badger's quick throw,
Beats squirrel, beats the weasels,
Neatly nutmegs a vole
And fools the diving keeper
With a right-foot scorcher. Goal!

And now the presentation –
The hare receives the cup,
And just listen to that cheering
As he grins and holds it up!
The final score again: 2 – 1,
In a brilliant match, and so
From Wembley Wood at midnight,
It's back to the studio . . .

Nathaniel

Nathaniel woke up yawning,
'I'm half asleep,' he said,
So his left half went down to breakfast
And his right half stayed in bed.

Mr Williams

The green scarf,
Mr Williams,
Hanging behind your door,
Thinks it's a snake.

Be careful,
Mr Williams,
Treat your green scarf kindly,
Treat it well.

Don't crush it,
Mr Williams,
Don't trail it in the dirt,
Don't sit on it.

The green scarf,
Mr Williams,
Hanging behind your door,
Thinks it's a snake.

The Lugworm and the Haddock

Said the lugworm from its burrow
To the haddock in the sea,
'How'd you like a worm for dinner?
Well, you won't catch little me,'
And it laughed and wriggled round
Safely hidden underground.

Said the haddock to the lugworm
'It's a miracle to me
How you make those cunning burrows
In the sand beneath the sea.
I could never dig one, never,
But you lugworms, you're so clever!'

Said the lugworm, swelling proudly,
'If you're good, I'll let you see
How we start to dig our tunnels
So deep down and cleverly.
Wait one moment, up I come,'
'Gulp,' the haddock said. 'Yum, yum.'

Don't Blame Me

When the plastic dinosaur
Jumped out of the cornflake box
And tipped a load of cornflakes
Into my sister's tea –
Nobody saw it happen,
Except me.

When the felt-tipped pen
Flew round my bedroom,
Drawing on the walls
Blue pictures of the sea –
Nobody saw it happen,
Except me.

And nobody saw it happen
When a grape zoomed from the fruitbowl
And landed slap bang wallop
In my Uncle Henry's ear –
I get the blame for everything
Round here.

One Dark Night

Little Granny Witherspoon was sitting, knitting,
  rocking,
When steps crunched on the path outside and
  someone started knocking,
'Now who on earth can that be on a night so wild
  and raw?'
Said Granny, shuffling down the hall towards her
  cottage door.

The stranger in the front porch grinned, 'I wonder
  if I might
Just step inside to warm myself. It's bitter out
  tonight.'
'Of course,' said Granny. 'Please, come in and
  shelter from the rain.
There, sit close to the fire, my dear. What was
  your name again?'

'My name? Er . . . Wolf,' the stranger answered,
  moving to a chair,
His jaw was long, he had a hungry look and thick
  grey hair.
'You'll have some tea,' said Granny kindly. 'Take
  this last cup, do,
While I pop to the kitchen and put on another brew.'

She left. The stranger licked his lips and raised the
   dainty cup,
He'd have his tea and then, perhaps, a snack to
   fill him up.
He sighed contentedly and sipped. He glanced
   around the room,
Then sat bolt upright . . . thirteen wolf heads
   glared down from the gloom!

Yes, thirteen wolf heads, glass-eyed, varnished,
   stuffed and mounted, dead.
He sprang up from his chair to leave. 'Don't go,
   dear,' Granny said.
She looked so sweet in fluffy slippers, hair in a
   neat grey bun,
And holding – not a tray of tea and biscuits – but
   a gun . . .

The storm howls round the cottage walls, the
   wild winds sweep and moan,
But Granny in her tiny cottage never feels alone,
She turns the lights down, rakes the coals,
   whispers a quiet 'Night night',
And fourteen wolf heads grin back in the embers'
   dying light.

The Comet and the Moon

'Tell me,' said the comet,
As it whooshed past the moon's pale face,
'Why do you look so sulky
As you make your way through space?'

'You'd sulk as well,' the moon said,
'If you were doomed, like me,
To always plod the same path
In the chains of gravity.

You're free to flare and sizzle,
You roam like rockets do,
While I'm stuck here in orbit
Of the Earth . . . I envy you.

Once things were better – spacemen
Came up to float and walk
And scratch my back. Now life's too dull,
So comet, stay and talk.'

The comet didn't answer,
Already it had gone
To wag it's tail round Venus
While the moon trudged on.

Eileen Idle

Eileen Idle's eyebrows,
The hairiest of features,
Make the perfect hiding place
For small shy creatures.

Deep in Eileen's eyebrows
Fieldmice meet for talks,
And wrens enjoy a game of cards
Safe from sparrowhawks.

Ambition

I, said the first man,
Will build the tallest building ever,
Taller than the Sears Tower
And with the smoothest elevators
To get you to the top
Almost before you've left the ground.
Eagles will nest on it,
It will wear my name in gold, like a crown,
And people, when they stare up from the street,
Will marvel.

I, said the second man,
Will build the fastest car ever,
Faster than sound, than lightning
And with the best acceleration
To get you to your destination
Almost before you've left home.
Special roads will be constructed for it,
It will wear my name in diamonds on the
    dashboard,
And people, when they see it blurring past,
Will gasp.

I, said Lily,
Will build the funniest hat ever
All pink and wobbly like a plateful of jelly,
With knitted ear flaps and eye holes to spy
    through
And a parrot on top which flutters
When you pull a string,
And people, when they see me in it,
Will laugh so much they'll lie down on the floor
And kick their legs in the air
Like little babies.

In a Narrow Place

In a narrow place
In the cold north woods,
Two caribou
Came face to face.

Said one: 'This track
Will not allow
Us both to pass
So, you, go back!'

The second caribou
Replied:
'Go back yourself,
I'm coming through.'

The first said 'Right,
You've had your chance,
If you won't move,
We'll have to fight.'

Heads down, they clashed
And all the woods
Echoed as
Their antlers crashed.

They shoved and strained
And shoved some more,
But both were strong
So neither gained.

'Look here,' one said,
'We're dopes, you know,
To end up fighting
Head to head,

So I'll reverse
And you come on,
Until we find
A place to pass.'

'But why should you
Give in to me?'
Replied the other
Caribou.

'I'll back.' 'No, me.'
'No, me!' 'No, me!'
'I'll fight you if
You don't agree.'

Once more they clashed,
Once more the woods
Echoed as
Their antlers crashed . . .

And so it goes:
They fight, they talk,
They fight again,
Nose pressed to nose.

And who will win?
'Ah, we will win,'
Whisper the grey wolves,
Closing in.

Clearing Out

On Monday
There were skeletons under my bed,
I tickled them out with a feather duster
And locked them in the wardrobe.

On Tuesday
There were snakes under my bed,
I wrestled them into granny knots
And locked them in the wardrobe.

On Wednesday
There were scorpions under my bed,
I lured them out with a trail of honey
And locked them in the wardrobe.

On Thursday
There were ghosts under my bed,
I bundled them up like newspapers
And locked them in the wardrobe.

On Friday
We moved to our new house,
Packing everything into the lorry,
Leaving only the wardrobe behind.

The Witches Are All on Strike

The witches are all on strike.

Spells? No one to say them.
Curses? No one to lay them.
Pointed hat makers? No one to pay them.

The witches are all on strike.

Warlocks? In distress.
Warts? Try the NHS.
Children who wander into gingerbread houses?
Couldn't care less.

The witches are all on strike.

Brooms? Gathering dust.
Cauldrons? Collecting rust.
Suppliers of newts and frogs? Going bust.

The witches are all on strike.

Toads? Creeping away.
Black cats? Starting to stray.
Blasted heaths at midnight under a full moon?
Safe as day.

The Cow in the Storm

The sky turned grey,
The horse went 'Neigh',
But the cow just went on chewing.

The sky turned black,
The ducks went 'Quack',
But the cow just went on chewing.

Lightning sparked,
The farm dog barked,
But the cow just went on chewing.

Thunder clapped,
The chickens flapped,
But the cow just went on chewing.

Raindrops splashed,
The farm cat dashed,
But the cow just went on chewing.

Showers stopped,
Rabbits hopped,
But the cow just went on chewing.

The sky turned blue,
I hopped too,
But the cow just went on chewing.

Sunshine streamed,
The whole farm steamed,
But the cow,
The cow,
The cow,
The cow,
But the cow just went on chewing.

Awake, Asleep

Awake from hibernation
The bear nosed through the wood,
Ate bulbs and roots and snails –
Everything tasted good,
Ate shoots and fruits and wasp nests,
Ate ants' eggs for a treat,
Ate cranberries, bilberries, crowberries –
Everything tasted sweet.

Awake from hibernation,
The bear nosed through the trees,
Ate salmon from the rivers,
Ate honey from the bees,
Ate till the leaves turned rusty
And the cold mists swirled,
Came to a cave, remembered,
And vanished from the world.

A Visit to Harley Street

Oh, help me, doctor, help me, please!
I've caught a dose of tee-hee-hees,
These wretched giggles won't let go . . .
Tee hee, ha ha, ho ho ho ho!
Oh, do excuse me . . . It's not right,
They keep me wide awake all night,
Give me some tablets, anything
To stop this . . . tee hee . . . chuckling.
Oh dear! It started when I saw
My Uncle on the kitchen floor,
He'd slipped . . . ho ho . . . on something
    wet . . .
Oh, tee hee hee . . . I can't forget
The way he looked, sprawled out down there
Completely bald, yes, not one hair –
His hair, you see, was not his own,
He wore a wig, and that had flown . . .
Ha ha ha . . . like a frizbee, swish,
And landed, splat, in doggy's dish,
And ever since I saw that sight –
My Uncle's fall, his wig's wild flight –
I've had these fits of tee-hee-hees,
Oh, help me, doctor, help me, please!

The doctor nodded twice and then
Reached for his writing pad and pen –
'You need, as hiccup sufferers do,
A sudden shock to pull you through.
I think I've got the very thing
To help you,' he said, scribbling.
'Take this, my bill.' It made me wince.
Six hundred pounds! I've not laughed since.

The Magic Drum

I've got a drum,
A magic drum,
I mustn't bash
Or boff it,
For if I did
The spinning world
Would stop
And I'd fall off it.

Over to Our Reporter on the Front Line . . .

. . . It was a surprise attack
Coming in from the south
While the city was asleep.
One by one, parks, gardens,
Streets and squares,
Were quietly taken out,
And by daybreak
It seemed all over.

But then the resistance began.
Men with trucks,
Women at their gates with brooms
Fought bravely back,
And despite reports that children
Had welcomed the invader,
In less than half a day
The enemy lay beaten
Or was driven underground
Into the drains.

All's quiet now on the streets.
I've been outside
And people are emerging
From their homes.
But as one old lady told me,
'We're not safe yet. You can never be sure.
Spring's a long way off, –
Blooming snow!'

Professor Mysterious

Professor Mysterious stood at his window
Listening as birds twittered sweetly outside,
'I know what I'll do, I'll invent a new brew
To make people sing just like the birdies,' he
    cried.

Professor Mysterious in his laboratory
Weighed out some peanuts and birdseed and
    bread
And mixed them with water and whisked them
    till, 'That ought to
Do it,' Professor Mysterious said.

Professor Mysterious sat down to dinner,
'Do try this new drink dear,' he said to his wife,
'It's really nutritious, you'll find it deliciously
Tasty and, who knows, it might change your life.'

Professor Mysterious watched his wife closely,
She sipped but did not start to whistle or tweet,
So sad and quite weary, Professor Mysterious
Trudged up to bed and fell deeply asleep.

Professor Mysterious woke the next morning
And went down to breakfast – his wife wasn't
  there,
He looked in the larder, the lounge, he looked
  harder
Upstairs in the attic and under the stair.

Professor Mysterious searched round the garden,
Where could she have gone? Then he heard a
  loud squawk,
A whistle, a screech, and saw, perched out of
  reach,
His wife on the ridge of the roof like a hawk.

She was covered in feathers and, oh, she looked
  lovely
From green pointed tail to the tip of her beak,
'Please, don't fly away!' the Professor yelled.
  'Stay!'
And he rushed back inside, though his legs felt
  quite weak.

He poured out some bird-mixture, gulped it and
  waited,
And soon he was perched by his wife's downy side,
They moved to the gutter from where, with a
  flutter,
They took off together and started to glide.

In long sweeping circles, they drifted up higher
Till houses were shrunk into small dots below,
Then meeting a swallow, turned southwards to
    follow,
Migrating away from the onset of snow.

Ten thousand miles later, beyond the equator,
They landed where zebras and elephants roam,
And looking quite serious, Mrs Mysterious,
Ruffled her crest and said, 'Let's make this home.'

They nested high up in a thorny acacia,
And now with five fledgelings they twitter and tweet
And live out their days where the wildebeest graze,
Eating lizards and snakes in the African heat.

Finding Out about the Family

It was really rather scary
When my dear old Auntie Mary
Started going very hairy
When the moon was full and bright,
And went outside on the prowl
With a loud and eerie howl
Like a wild wolf on a hilltop
In the middle of the night.

It was really rather odd
When I found my Uncle Tod
Dangling from a wooden rod
Where a curtain usually hangs,
He was upside down, in black,
With his hair slicked thinly back,
And the firelight flickering fiercely
On the sharp tips of his fangs.

It was most bizarre of all
When my little brother Paul
Disappeared into the wall
In a puff of purple smoke,
Then my sister waved her wand,
And now I'm living in this pond
Eating flies and feeling slimy . . .
Ribbit ribbit, croak croak croak.

Andy Handy

Andy Handy's legs are bandy,
Almost like a O,
Through Andy Handy's bandy legs
The trains to Scotland go.

There Were These Woodworm

So funny they were –
All wriggly and squiggly –
And such good performers!
Munching away in the old theatre
At beams and stairs and props and chairs and the
    box office and
the stage and the circle and the stalls and the
    walls and the
wings and the doors and the window frames and
    the joists in the
roof and the joists in the floors . . .

For years they kept at it,
Night after night,
Day after day,
And so funny they were –
All wriggly and squiggly –
And such good performers that
At last

They brought the house down.

Moira Murray

Moira Murray, small and neat,
Grown up shoes on tiny feet,
Grown up clothes: smart blouse and skirt,
Not a single trace of dirt.
Moira Murray's mother: 'You'd
Never think of being rude,
Never make your parents sad,
Would you, Moira?' Moira's Dad:
'Keep away from games and noise,
Friends are dangerous, especially boys.'

Moira Murray, properly,
Sits and takes her lonely tea,
Tucks her elbows in and eats,
Hears the children in the streets.

Moira Murray goes upstairs,
Kneels down quietly, says her prayers,
Jumps in bed, turns off the light,
Cries her eyes out every night.

Whose Job It Is

A man came to my door,
He wore a badge which read –
The person whose job it is to order other people
   about –
He cleared his throat and said,
'You must leave your house
And go out into the street.'

'Why?' I asked. He frowned,
'That's not for me to say.
I'm just the person whose job it is to order other
   people about,
I speak, and you obey.
Now kindly leave your house
And go out into the street.'

'I won't,' I said. He sighed
And scratched his forehead, 'Please!
I am only doing my job as the person whose job it
   is to order other people about.'
He got down on his knees,
'I beg you to leave your house
And go out into the street.'

I shook my head. He sobbed,
Kneeling in the dirt,
'What if I give you the person whose job it is to
   order other people about badge,' he said,
'To fasten on your shirt,
Then will you leave your house
And go out into the street?'

I pinned the bright badge on.
The man got up and smiled,
And shook my hand and went off skipping,
Skipping like a child,
While I, the person whose job it is to order other
   people about,
Left my house
And went out into the street.

The Wildfowler's Nightmare

I am the ghost of the duck you shot
And plucked and simmered in your pot.

I am the duck returned to claim
Revenge on you for taking aim.

You fired the gun. You loosed the lead
That stung my poor defenceless head.

I am the ghost of the duck come back
To haunt you with a whispered quack,

A beat of phantom wings, a peck,
Soft as a cold kiss on your neck.

You can't hide. In your briefest nap
You'll hear my quiet approaching flap,

I'll hunt you through the endless deep
Marshlands of your lonely sleep.

I'm your nightmare now, your fear,
Rustling dry feathers in your ear,

Tracking you down, no matter what,
I am the ghost of the duck you shot.

Shaggy Dogs

Two sheepdogs in a field
Looked up and wondered why
A great big flock of woolly sheep
Was cluttering up the sky.

The sheepdogs growled and leapt,
And climbed the slopes of air,
Yapping, snarling, nipping, snapping,
Scattering sheep everywhere.

And when the sky was clear again
They hurried home together
Back to their field to sunbathe
In the warm blue weather.

Benny Penny

Benny Penny met a monkey,
Benny Penny said,
'Why don't you be me today?
I'll be you instead.'

'Sounds good,' said the monkey,
Pointing to a tree,
'You go that way, I'll go this,
Meet you after tea.'

Monkey in the classroom
Writing ABCs,
Pen too small and fiddly,
Rather have the trees.

Benny in the branches
Swaying near the sky,
Leaves taste sour and stringy,
Rather have meat pie.

Monkey in a muddle,
Two plus two is one,
Angry teacher coming,
Run, monkey, run.

Benny in a clearing,
Dazzled by the sun,
Hungry tiger coming,
Run, Benny, run.

Benny meets the monkey
Halfway back to town,
Monkey climbs back in the trees,
Benny's glad he's down.

Benny waves, the monkey
Waves back and is gone,
Benny runs home whistling
And the world spins on.

Sow What

Molly planted cabbage seed
And grew a patch of greens,
Polly planted bean seed
And grew a row of beans,
Dolly planted carrot seed
And grew a clump of carrots,
Wally planted bird seed
And grew a flock of parrots.

Witch of the Waterland

Wet's my country,
Here I stand,
I am the Witch of the Waterland,
Robed in eelskin,
Housed in reeds,
Stirring a cauldron of waterweeds,
Fill a deep ditch,
Let me soak,
Soothe me to sleep with a marsh frog's croak.

Wet's my country,
Here I stand,
I am the Witch of the Waterland,
Some have black cats,
I have coots,
Fen-familiars – moorhens, newts,
Webbed things, finned things,
Things that like
Ducking, diving: otters, pike.

Wet's my country,
Here I stand,
I am the Witch of the Waterland,
Things that please me:

Rings of moss,
Bog to dance on, swamps to cross,
Things I conjure:
Streams in flood,
Springs that bubble, slides of mud.

Wet's my country;
Here I stand,
I am the Witch of the Waterland,
Lightning, sizzle!
Thunder, crash!
Heaven, spout and downpour splash!
Brim all gutters!
Burst each drain!
My favourite spell is a spell of rain,
Wet's my country,
Here I stand,
I am the Witch of the Waterland.

Miss Antrobus

Why do you love your octopus,
Miss Antrobus, Miss Antrobus?
Why do you love your octopus,
Miss Antrobus, my dear?

I love my octopus because
It hugs me and it wriggles,
I love my octopus because
Its wriggles give me giggles,
I love my octopus because
It juggles jars of pickles,
I love my octopus because
It tickles, oh, it tickles!

Mammoths

There were mammoths in our garden last night.
What else explains
The clothesline snapped by something very
   strong,
The puddles shaped
Like huge feet stamped into the lawn, and all
That white blossom
Shaken from the pear tree? What else explains
The trampled rose
And the noise I heard under my window –
Huff-puffing like
A steam train going uphill in the dark?
Oh yes, there were
Mammoths in our garden last night, though these
Small signs would not
Be recognized by everyone, only
Specialists know
What to look for, only mammoth experts,
People like me.

A Bargain

The prince said to the pretty girl
'I think I'll let you be
My bride, my wife, my helpmate,
If you'll simply agree
To have ten children, mend my socks,
Cook kippers for my tea,
Wash out my dirty underwear,
And never nag at me.'

The pretty girl said to the prince,
'You need a wife. I see.
All right, I'll be your partner,
If you'll simply agree
To bring me back last Monday
From the dry part of the sea,
A pair of blue bananas
And a toffee apple tree.'

My Pet Mouth

I had a pet mouth. We liked to chat,
We'd talk about this, we'd talk about that,
All day long.

I had a pet mouth. We liked to eat,
We'd share a pizza for a treat,
Delicious!

I had a pet mouth. We liked to play:
Tongue twisters, word games, trying to say
Things backwards.

I had a pet mouth. It grew too proud,
It answered back and laughed out loud
When I shooshed it.

I had a pet mouth. It grew too wild,
It stuck out its tongue like a naughty child,
It blew raspberries.

I had a pet mouth. It wouldn't obey
So I opened the door and shooed it away –
Good riddance!

I had a pet mouth. I'm better alone,
You don't have fights when you're on your own,
Life's more peaceful.

I had a pet mouth. I'm well rid of it,
There's more time now to read or to sit
And watch telly.

I've bought a pet dog, Lucky's his name,
We go to the park, but it isn't the same,
Not really.

I had a pet mouth . . .

Magroodle Said

Magroodle said, 'I'm an honest chef,
The truth is what should matter,
My toad in the hole *is* toad in the hole –
A real toad cooked in batter.'

Magroodle said, 'For fancy food
I do not care a hoot,
Beef Wellington *is* Beef Wellington –
Raw beef in a rubber boot.'

The police came for Magroodle,
Forensics took his knife,
His shepherd's pie *was* shepherd's pie –
Magroodle's doing life.

Windfalls

'These apples,' said the wasp,
'Though bruised, are not yet oozy,
I'll come back in a day or two
And drink until I'm woozy
And satisfy my thirst.'

But somebody got there first.

'These pears,' said the blackbird,
'Are too green to digest,
I'll come back in a day or two
And when they're at their best
My beak will do its worst.'

But somebody got there first.

'These plums,' said the hedgehog,
'Could be a touch more sweet,
I'll come back in a day or two
And eat and eat and eat
Until I'm fit to burst.'

But somebody
But somebody
But somebody got there first.

Blankets

Slim sleeps under
A red and white blanket,
Striped like a pair of pajamas.

Rosa sleeps under
A yellow blanket,
Spun from the wool of llamas.

Innuk sleeps under
A furry blanket
Stitched from the skins of bears.

Bud sleeps under
An army blanket –
Rat holes, patches, tears.

Tsai sleeps under
A dragon blanket
Sewn by an emperor's daughter.

I sleep under
A silver blanket
Made by a wizard from water.

Little Cissie Wilson

Little Cissie Wilson
Woke one day in bed
Changed into a caterpillar,
Little Cissie said,
'Mummy, I'm a caterpillar,
Tell me what this means!'
Mrs Wilson answered,
'At last you'll eat your greens.'

The Anaconda

The anaconda stretches a long long long long way – Its head is in tomorrow, while its tail's still in today.

Breakfast for One

The cafe was crowded. I was joined by a bloke
Who looked at my breakfast and tutted and
    spoke:
'Consider that sausage,' he said. 'Think of that –
Its future your teeth and its past boiling fat.
And how must that fried egg feel? Hopelessly
    glum –
So nearly a chicken, now bound for your tum,
And that bacon – once happy, a pig, plump and
    pink –
You surely can't eat that; just stop and just
    think.'

I put down my knife and stared at the plate.
The fried egg stared back, but it wasn't too late.
'You're quite right,' I cried. 'Take this breakfast
    away!'
And I'd got up to leave when I heard the bloke
    say:
'It's a pity to waste it though, seeing it's still
    hot . . .'
And in less than five minutes, he'd swallowed the
    lot!

Old Alf

Old Alf, an indecisive chap,
Once put an ant down on a map
And said, 'Wherever you shall be
When I have counted thirty-three
Is where I'll spend my holiday
This year.' Well, what a thing to say!
And what a holiday he had:
Depressing, smelly, sodden, sad –
Two weeks inside a leaking tent
Near Gravesend sewage farm, in Kent.

Just for Fun

It started with a cactus
From a boot sale, just for fun,
But the cactus looked so lonely
That she bought another one,
Then another, then a cheese plant,
Then some fuchsias, then a fern,
Till Belinda's rooms were bursting –
There was hardly room to turn.

Aspidistras, palms, geraniums, lilies –
More and more and more,
Jasmine creeping through the bathroom,
Ivy trailing on the floor,
'Oooh, how lovely!' said her neighbours,
'It's the prettiest house we've seen.'
'Take some cuttings,' said Belinda,
'We can turn the whole street green.'

Soon each house was like a garden,
Tendrils twined themselves in knots,
Climbed the stairs, explored the attics,
Burst like smoke from chimney pots,
Roots went rootling through the cellars,
Shoots went shooting everywhere,
Huge leaves shouldered up the roof tiles
And escaped into the air.

Down the high street, past the station,
Moved the jungle like a tide,
Chasing shoppers out of Tesco's,
Shoving cars and trucks aside,
Swamping parks, devouring statues,
Rolling on and on and on,
Till the last grey wall was swallowed
And the last grey roof was gone.

First arrivals were some fruit bats,
Then a parakeet flew down
And the howls of monkeys echoed
Round what once had been a town.
Tigers prowl the crumbling ruins,
Tree snakes slither in the sun . . .
And all because Belinda
Bought a cactus, just for fun.

Joe Bright

By day, shut in his workshop,
Joe Bright cuts bits of tin,
And smooths them out and flattens them
Until they're paper thin.

At dusk Joe Bright flies skywards
With boxes, bags and jars,
And on the branches of the dark
He hangs a million stars.